W9-BMJ-730

STOCKING STUMPERS

CHICAGO CUBS

By S. Claus

RED-LETTER PRESS, INC.
Saddle River, New Jersey

Red-Letter Press, Inc.
P.O. Box 393, Saddle River, NJ 07458
www.Red-LetterPress.com
info@Red-LetterPress.com

ACKNOWLEDGMENTS
SANTA'S SUBORDINATE CLAUSES

Compiled By:
Steve Fiorentine

Editor:
Jack Kreismer

Contributor:
Jeff Kreismer

Cover Design:
Cliff Behum

Special Mention:
Sparky Anderson Kreismer

INTRODUCTION

Whether you're having a few quiet
moments to yourself or enjoying a
reunion with friends and family, Stocking
Stumpers is the perfect holiday companion.
Gather 'round the Christmas tree or simply
kick back in your easy chair while
trying out the holiday humdingers,
tailor-made tests and trivia tidbits.

Once you've had a sampling, I think you'll
agree, Stocking Stumpers is proof of the
Christmas pudding that good things do
come in small packages. Ho ho ho!

Merry Christmas!!

S. Claus

The Mantle Meter

'Tis right around Christmas
and all through the book,

There are all sorts of stumpers
everywhere that you look.

There are quizzes and seasonal tests
to take you to task,

But what are those "stocking"
questions you ask?

Well, the stockings are hung
by the chimney with care.

The more that are filled,
the tougher the bear.

And so it is that
the Mantle Meter keeps score,

Rating the stumpers,
one stocking or more.

STOCKING STUMPERS

CHICAGO CUBS

FIRST PITCH

1. What pitcher has the most Opening Day starts in Cubs history?

2. In what year did the Cubs become the first team in baseball history to win back-to-back World Series titles?
a) 1898 b) 1908 c) 1918 d) 1928

3. Who was the first player to steal five bases in a game for the Cubs: Lou Brock, Eric Young, or Shawon Dunston?

4. With the dawning of interleague play in 1997, who was the first player to serve as designated hitter for the Cubs?

5. Who was the first player to play for the Cubs to be inducted into the National Baseball Hall of Fame?

In 1994, what Cub became the first National League player to hit three home runs on Opening Day?

Answers

1.

Ferguson Jenkins (7 openers)

2.

B

3.

Eric Young, on May 14, 2000, against the Montreal Expos in a 16-15 defeat

4.

Dave Clark

5.

Grover Cleveland Alexander (1938)

Tuffy Rhodes

HISTORY 101

1. Can you come up with any of the three names the Chicago National League franchise went by before being dubbed the Cubs in 1902 and officially adopting the nickname in 1907?

2. The Cubs only two World Series victories came over what American League team?

3. What outside the box coaching method did Cubs Owner P.K. Wrigley experiment with from 1960-65?

4. In what year did the Cubs clinch their lone wild card berth: 1998, 2003, or 2008?

5. The Cubs recorded the franchise's milestone 10,000th victory on the road at which visiting ballpark?

What Cub had more hits, doubles and sacrifice flies in the 1990s than anyone else in Major League Baseball?

Answers

1.

White Stockings, Colts and Orphans

2.

Detroit Tigers

3.

The team did not have a manager. Instead, they used a collection of coaches referred to as the "College of Coaches."

4.

1998

5.

Coors Field

Mark Grace

MANAGER MANIA

1. What National Baseball Hall of Fame inductee served as the first manager in franchise history? (Hint: Think basketball, as in sporting goods.)

2. Three managers were named National League Manager of the Year with the Cubs. How many do you know?

3. What Hall of Famer holds the career record for wins as a Cubs manager?

4. What manager, noted for his controversial style, was hired in 1965, signaling the end of the "College of Coaches" experiment?

5. The Cubs won their two World Series titles under what Hall of Fame player-manager who was part of the famed Tinker to Evers to Chance double play combo?

In 1938, who hit the famed "Homer in the Gloamin'" against the Pittsburgh Pirates that put the Cubs in first place and propelled them to the National League pennant?

ANSWERS

1. Albert Spalding (co-founder of the Spalding Company, sporting goods makers and the manufacturer of the official NBA basketball)

2. Jim Frey, Don Zimmer and Lou Piniella

3. Cap Anson (1,282 wins)

4. "Leo the Lip" Durocher

5. Frank Chance

Gabby Hartnett

BASEBALL'S FIRST DYNASTY

1. What was the peculiar outcome of Game 1 of the 1907 World Series between the Cubs and Tigers?

2. What Hall of Fame pitcher of "digital distinction" threw a complete game shutout for the Cubs in the deciding fifth game of the 1907 Series?

3. The Cubs limited what Tigers legend to a measly .200 batting average during the '07 Series?

4. What infamous blunder allowed the Cubs to win the National League pennant and return to the World Series in 1908?

5. What was significant about the crowd watching the Cubs 1908 World Series-clinching Game 5 victory at Detroit?

❄ SEASONAL STUMPER ❄

This Christmas baby was born on December 25, 1980, and grew up to become a 16-year big leaguer who had two stints as a noted second baseman with the Cubs, from 1975-78 and 1986-88. Can you name him?

ANSWERS

1.
The game ended in a 3-3 tie in the 12th inning when the contest had to be called for darkness.

2.
Mordecai "Three Finger" Brown

3.
Ty Cobb

4.
New York Giants first baseman Fred Merkle's base running error, whose gaffe is now known as "Merkle's Boner"

5.
Not much... It was the lowest attended game in World Series history- 6,210.

Seasonal Stumper Answer:

Manny Trillo

CURSED

1. The Cubs have not won a World Series since 1908, which is the longest title drought in professional sports. Fans blame this on what superstitious reason?

2. What phrase did Billy Goat Tavern owner William Sianis mutter upon learning that his pet goat could not enter Wrigley Field with him for Game 4 of the 1945 World Series?

3. What is the supposed reason why Cubs owner P.K. Wrigley did not permit Sianis to bring his goat with him?

4. Sianis allegedly sent a telegram to Wrigley after the Cubs lost the 1945 World Series in seven games to the Detroit Tigers saying what?

5. According to Sianis' nephew Sam Sianis, how are the Cubs supposed to reverse the curse?

In the 2003 NLCS, what player hit the first grand slam in Cubs playoff history?

ANSWERS

1.

The Curse of the Billy Goat

2.

"The Cubs ain't gonna win no more."

3.

The goat's unpleasant stench

4.

"Who stinks now?"

5.

They must admit goats into
Wrigley Field because they sincerely
want to and not just for the publicity.

Aramis Ramirez

LOVABLE LOSERS

1.
In 1969, the Cubs blew a nine and a half game division lead over what team?

2. 1977 proved to be one of the biggest collapses in team history as the Cubs had an 8½ game NL East lead on June 28, only to finish the season at 81-81, 20 games behind what team?

3. In the seventh inning of Game 5 of the 1984 NLCS, what Cub let a ground ball go through his legs to allow the tying run to score and spur a Padres series victory?

4. Only five outs away from a World Series berth in 2003, what momentum-swinging incident is blamed for triggering a Marlins game-winning rally in Game 6 of the NLCS?

5. As part of their 2003 NLCS Game 6 meltdown, what Cub botched a ground ball off of the bat of Miguel Cabrera, which could have ended the inning?

In what should have served as a bad omen for the Cubs, what ran onto the field during a 1969 game at Shea Stadium and circled Ron Santo, who was in the on deck circle?

ANSWERS

1.

New York Mets

2.

Philadelphia Phillies

3.

Leon Durham

4. Cubs fan Steve Bartman interfered with a foul ball hit near the left field stands, preventing Moises Alou from making the catch and the second out of the inning.

5.

Alex Gonzalez

A black cat

THE ONE AND ONLY

1. What Cub is the only player in MLB history to have three seasons of 60 or more home runs?

2. As the most expensive signing in team history, who is the only player to receive a contract exceeding $100 million from the Cubs?

3. Who is the only Cubs third baseman to win a Gold Glove award?

4. What player is the only Cub to hit five grand slams in a single season?

5. In 2002, what switch-hitting Cub became the only National League player ever to homer from both sides of the plate in the same inning?

Due to Hurricane Ike, Carlos Zambrano pitched the first-ever no-hitter at a neutral site in 2008. Where did the game take place?

ANSWERS

1.

Sammy Sosa

2.

Alfonso Soriano

3.

Ron Santo

4.

Ernie Banks (1955)

5.

Mark Bellhorn

Miller Park, in Milwaukee

THE RECORD BOOKS

1. This Cub's 191 RBIs is the major league record for RBIs in a single season. Who is he?

2. In 1998, what Cubs rookie pitcher tied the major league record for strikeouts in a single game with 20?

3. What player amassed a record 18 Gold Gloves over his career, with six of them coming as a member of the Cubs?

4. In 2012, what Cub broke Ryne Sandberg's NL record of 123 consecutive games at second base without an error before tying Placido Polanco's MLB record 141-game streak?

5. What Cub holds the record for most intentional walks in a single game with five in a 16-inning contest?

❄ SEASONAL STUMPER ❄

What Cubs pitcher, whose name is very similar to the crooner of *The Christmas Song*, went 20-4 in 1910 while also leading the National League with a 1.80 ERA?

Answers

1.

Hack Wilson (1930)

2.

Kerry Wood

3.

Greg Maddux

4.

Darwin Barney

5.

Andre Dawson

Seasonal Stumper Answer:

King Cole
(Nat King Cole is the singer.)

TWO OF A KIND

1. What Cubs brother tandem paired together to throw a shutout against the Los Angeles Dodgers in 1975, becoming the first pair of brothers to do so?

2. Only two Cubs left-handed pitchers have tossed no-hitters. One was Walter Thornton, way back in 1898. Who's the other?

3. What relievers are the only two Cubs to record over 50 saves in a single season?

4. What two Cubs played in all 164 games of the 1965 season, when Chicago played two extra contests because of ties?

5. What two Cubs pitchers appeared on the cover of a 2003 edition of *Sports Illustrated* together and were nicknamed "Chicago Heat?"

Legendary Cubs announcer Harry Caray dubbed what rabid Cubs fan "Leather Lungs" for his ability to holler for hours on end?

ANSWERS

1.

Rick and Paul Reuschel

2.

Ken Holtzman, in 1969 against
the Braves (Curiously, he did
not strike out a batter.)

3.

Randy Myers and Rod Beck

4.

Ron Santo and Billy Williams

5.

Mark Prior and Kerry Wood

Ronnie "Woo Woo" Wickers

A GLOBAL GAME

1. What Cubs slugger is the all-time home run leader for players born outside of the United States of America?

2. What Dominican-born player hit a three-run homer in his first big league at bat and set the record for most RBIs in a major league debut with six?

3. Serving as a true pioneer, this Cub was the first Puerto Rican to play in the major leagues. Was it: Hiram Bithorn, Carmelo Martinez or Hector Lezcano?

4. What Cub is the only Canadian-born player inducted into the National Baseball Hall of Fame?

5. In 1996, what Cubs player became the first major leaguer born in Singapore?

Seven years after he was hit in the head in his only major league at-bat, what former Cub returned to the major leagues in 2012 with the Miami Marlins for another at-bat?

ANSWERS

1.

Sammy Sosa

2.

Starlin Castro

3.

Hiram Bithorn

4.

Ferguson Jenkins

5.

Robin Jennings

Adam Greenberg

Mr. Cub

1. Ernie Banks played for what Negro American League team before joining the Cubs?

2. True or False? Banks is the only shortstop in MLB history to win back-to-back MVP honors.

3. Banks' 2,528 games played as a Cub is a franchise record. What other less desirable distinction does this represent?

4. For what reason might Ernie Banks have given Jim McGlothlin of the Reds a final "thank you"?

5. What was Banks' trademark catchphrase?

As a member of the New York Mets in 1976, who is believed to have hit the longest home run in Wrigley Field history?

ANSWERS

1.

Kansas City Monarchs

2.

True - in 1958 and 1959

3.

They are the most games played by a player without a trip to the playoffs.

4. McGlothlin was on the mound for the Reds on August 24, 1971, when Banks hit home run #512, the last of his career.

5.

"Let's play two!"

Dave Kingman, who launched an estimated 550-foot homer to left-center field

SCREEN TEST

1. In what 1986 film do a rebellious high school student and his friends skip school and attend a Cubs game at Wrigley Field?

2. Sammy Sosa made a cameo appearance as himself in what 2001 Chicago-based baseball movie?

3. In what 1993 children's movie do the Cubs sign a 12-year-old Little Leaguer to pitch for the team?

4. What classic 1992 film about a women's baseball league had scenes filmed at Wrigley Field?

5. The opening scene of what Jennifer Aniston - Vince Vaughn flick was filmed at Wrigley?

❄ SEASONAL STUMPER ❄

Hall of Famer Ralph Kiner played for the Cubs in 1953-54. Prior to that, he led the NL in homers for the Pirates for a record-setting span. If you know the number of "Swans a Swimming" in *The Twelve Days of Christmas*, then you know how many straight years Kiner led the Senior Circuit in HRs.

ANSWERS

1.

Ferris Beuller's Day Off

2.

Hardball

3.

Rookie of the Year

4.

A League of Their Own

5.

The Break-Up

Seasonal Stumper Answer:

Seven

BLOCKBUSTERS

1. In July of 2003, the Cubs acquired what slugger, who would become a franchise staple for almost nine seasons, along with Kenny Lofton from the Pittsburgh Pirates?

2. In exchange for Hee-Seop Choi and a minor leaguer, the Cubs acquired a first baseman fresh off a 2003 World Series title who became a two-time All-Star in Chicago. Who?

3. The Cubs traded what future Hall of Famer to the rival St. Louis Cardinals in 1964 as part of a package for Ernie Broglio, Doug Clemens and Bobby Shantz?

4. What other three teams were involved in the blockbuster four-way trade on July 31, 2004, that netted the Cubs star shortstop Nomar Garciaparra?

5. What outfielder who played seven years with Chicago was traded in 2013 for minor league pitcher Corey Black and cash to the Yankees, the team with which he'd begun his career?

In 1932, the Cubs became the final team to do what to their uniforms?

ANSWERS

1.

Aramis Ramirez

2.

Derrek Lee

3.

Lou Brock

4.

Boston Red Sox, Minnesota
Twins and Montreal Expos

5.

Alfonso Soriano

Add uniform numbers

NICKNAMES

1.
What pitcher nicknamed "The Red Baron" won the 1984 National League Cy Young Award as a member of the Cubs?

2.
What is Cap Anson's real first name?

3.
What Cubs pitcher with a fiery attitude went by the nicknames "Big Z" and "El Toro"?

4.
What outfielder, known as "Sarge", had a 15 year career and played with the Cubs from 1984-87, later serving as a coach?

5.
How did Mordecai Brown earn the nickname "Three Finger"?

What Cubs relief pitcher was famous for having six fingers on both of his hands?

ANSWERS

1.

Rick Sutcliffe

2.

Adrian

3.

Carlos Zambrano

4.

Gary Mathews

5.

He lost parts of two fingers on his right hand in a farm machinery mishap as a child.

Antonio Alfonseca

THERE'S A DRAFT IN HERE

1. Who did the Cubs draft with the first overall pick in the 1982 First-Year Player Draft?

2. In 2001, USC's Mark Prior was drafted #2 overall by the Cubs. What team drafted Prior out of high school in 1998 but didn't sign him to a contract?

3. The Cubs drafted what future NL Rookie of the Year with the Marlins in the eighth round of the 2000 First-Year Player Draft?

4. What two-time National League Cy Young Award winner did the Cubs draft in the 48th round of the 2003 First-Year Player Draft but fail to sign to a contract?

5. With the third pick in the 2006 Rule 5 Draft, the Cubs drafted what future MVP from the Devil Rays and subsequently sold him to the Reds?

What Cubs player hit the first-ever home run for Team USA in the World Baseball Classic?

ANSWERS

1.

Shawon Dunston

2.

New York Yankees

3.

Dontrelle Willis

4.

Tim Lincecum

5.

Josh Hamilton

Derrek Lee

Sweet Swingin' Billy

1. In what year was Billy Williams honored as the National League Rookie of the Year: 1958, 1961, or 1964?

2. Williams captured the NL batting title in 1972 with a .333 average, was second in RBIs, 122, and third in homers with 37. What player was the HR and RBI champ?

3. True or False? Williams never hit 20 or more home runs in consecutive seasons.

4. Williams held the National League record for consecutive game played until 1983. Who passed him?

5. After years of playing for the Cubs, what team did Williams finally make the playoffs with for the first time in 1975?

❄ Seasonal stumpeR ❄

On December 31, 2009, the Cubs got ready to ring in the New Year with a new outfielder, a free-agent they inked to a three-year, $15 million deal. He followed the signing with an All-Star year and played with Chicago until being traded to the Boston Red Sox in 2012. Who's "the word?"

ANSWERS

1.

1961

2.

Johnny Bench, 40 HRs and 125
RBIs (Nate Colbert was
second in homers with 38.)

3.

False - Williams hit 20 or more for
13 straight years (1961-73).

4.

Steve Garvey

5.

Oakland Athletics

Seasonal Stumper Answer:

"Byrd's the word" - Marlon Byrd

HOT STOVE

1. Who was Jed Hoyer's first free agent signing as Cubs general manager?

2. In January of 2004, the Cubs signed what pitcher coming off of Tommy John surgery, who would go on to excel in both the bullpen and starting rotation for the club?

3. The Cubs spent a record amount of money on free agents following the 2006 season. To the nearest "100 million," how much did they spend?

4. After signing a three-year, $30 million deal with the Cubs in 2009, what free agent bust was suspended in September of '09 and shipped to Seattle the following offseason?

5. What Cubs free agent signing in November of 1990 had won World Series rings with the Kansas City Royals and Cincinnati Reds?

After serving as interim manager in 2010, what manager was hired fulltime in 2011 but was fired after just one season by the new Theo Epstein regime?

ANSWERS

1.
David Dejesus

2.
Ryan Dempster

3.
300 million ($297.55 million, to be exact)

4.
Milton Bradley

5.
Danny Jackson (He made a third World Series appearance with the Phillies after being traded away.)

Mike Quade

Holy Cow!

1.
Name one of the three major league teams Harry Caray called games for prior to joining the Cubs broadcast booth.

2.
Caray took over for what other legendary Cubs play-by-play announcer?

3.
In 1989, Caray was honored with what prestigious award for baseball broadcasters?

4.
Caray became famous for his rendition of what song during the seventh-inning stretch?

5.
What phrase would go on to become Caray's signature home run call?

Sammy Sosa wore #21 as a member of the Cubs in honor of what hero from his youth?

ANSWERS

1.

St. Louis Cardinals, Oakland Athletics and Chicago White Sox

2.

Jack Brickhouse

3.

Ford C. Frick Award

4.

Take Me Out to the Ballgame

5.

"It might be... It could be... It is! A home run!"

Roberto Clemente

CLOSING TIME

1.
   Who is the Cubs all-time
   career leader in saves?

2. In 1993, Chicago's Randy Myers set a then
   NL record with 53 saves. Since then, Myers'
   mark has been matched or passed by three
   National League pitchers. Name them.

3.
   Who is the only Cub to start a game and
   rack up 30 saves in a single season?

4.
   What Cub is the only pitcher to
   be awarded the National League
   Cy Young Award as a reliever?

5. Carlos Marmol, who ranks second on the
   Cubs all-time saves list, became the
   fulltime closer for Chicago after taking
   over for whom during the 2009 season?

Who holds the Cubs record for
all-time home runs by a pitcher?

ANSWERS

1.

Lee Smith

2.

Trevor Hoffman,
John Smoltz and Eric Gagne

3.

Ryan Dempster (2005)

4.

Bruce Sutter (1979)

5.

Kevin Gregg

Carlos Zambrano, 23

INSULT TO INJURY

1. In 2004, Sammy Sosa had to go on the disabled list after suffering back spasms due to what bizarre occurrence?

2. What Cubs outfielder missed Opening Day in 1974 after claiming his eyelid was stuck from sleeping on it oddly?

3. In 2002, what Cubs relief pitcher broke his pinkie finger after getting it entangled in a chair?

4. What was Carlos Zambrano told to do in 2005 after experiencing discomfort in his pitching elbow?

5. What Cub had to be placed on the disabled list after bruising and spraining his knee while kicking an electric fan in the dugout?

❄ SEASONAL STUMPER ❄

The name of the most prominent chipmunk in that yuletide carol is the same as the first name of a third baseman who had a 14-year career in the National League, two of them with the Cubs, in 1958 and 1959.

ANSWERS

1.

He sneezed.

2.

Jose Cardenal

3.

Mike Remlinger

4.

He was advised to reduce the amount
of time he spent on the computer.

5.

Kyle Farnsworth

Seasonal Stumper Answer:

Alvin Dark

Either Or

1.

Which pitcher recorded more strikeouts as a Cub: Mark Prior or Kerry Wood?

2.

What Cubs center fielder once saved an American flag from being set on fire during a game: Rick Monday or Bob Dernier?

3.

Which slugger bashed more home runs in a Cubs uniform: Ernie Banks or Sammy Sosa?

4.

Which MVP winner had a higher slugging percentage as a member of the Cubs: Andre Dawson or Ryne Sandberg?

5.

Which recent Cubs manager had more wins while running the Cubs: Dusty Baker or Lou Piniella?

What player who holds the record for most teams played for by a position player donned a Cubs uniform during the 2001 season?

ANSWERS

1.

Kerry Wood

2. Monday- In a 1976 game at Dodger Stadium, two protestors jumped onto the field and were about to torch Old Glory, but he snatched it away from them.

3.

Sammy Sosa

4.

Andre Dawson

5.

Dusty Baker

Matt Stairs

ALL IN THE FAMILY

1. What father-son combination both played catcher for the Cubs?

2. Former Cub pitcher Dizzy Dean's brother had an equally loopy nickname. What was it?

3. What Cubs outfielder had his father, two uncles, and cousin play in the major leagues as well?

4. What pair of brothers played for the Cubs at different times, but played together while they were both members of the San Diego Padres?

5. In 2007, former owner Sam Zell sold the Cubs to what family?

Ryne Sandberg's nephew Jared played for what major league team from 2001-03?

ANSWERS

1.
Randy and Todd Hundley

2.
Paul "Daffy" Dean

3.
Moises Alou

4.
Jerry and Scott Hairston

5.
The Ricketts family

Tampa Bay Devil Rays

THE FRIENDLY CONFINES

1. Opened in 1914, Wrigley Field is the second oldest ballpark in the major leagues behind what other venue?

2. Wrigley Field was the last MLB ballpark to have lights installed, thus hosting 5,687 afternoon games in a row. In what year did the Cubs play their first home night game?

3. Since 1937, what is displayed at Wrigley Field after every Cubs home victory?

4. Chicago's Soldier Field is the NFL's oldest stadium. Which is older, Wrigley Field or Soldier Field?

5. Before being named Wrigley Field in 1926, what two prior names did the ballpark go by?

What Chicago anthem was written in 1984 by Steve Goodman?

ANSWERS

1.

Fenway Park

2.

1988

3.

Cubs Win Flag

4.

Wrigley

5.

Weeghman Park and Cubs Park

"Go, Cubs, Go!"

THE HOT CORNER

1. Ron Santo was the first third baseman to swat 300 home runs and collect five Gold Gloves. Who are the other two third basemen to accomplish this?

2. During the 1969 season, Santo stirred up controversy for performing what celebration after Cubs victories?

3. Ron Santo was the first player to wear what kind of headgear?

4. After 14 seasons with the Cubs, Santo was traded away to what team?

5. Santo held what position with the Cubs following his retirement from baseball?

❄ SEASONAL STUMPER ❄

Wrigley Field played host to what New Year's Day sporting tradition in 2009?

ANSWERS

1.

Mike Schmidt and Scott Rolen

2.

Heel click

3.

A batting helmet with ear flaps

4.

Chicago White Sox

5.

Radio broadcaster

Seasonal Stumper Answer:

The 2009 NHL Winter Classic between the
Chicago Blackhawks and Detroit Red Wings

RYNO

1. The Cubs landed a steal by acquiring future Hall of Famer Ryne Sandberg along with Larry Bowa from the Philadelphia Phillies for what journeyman shortstop?

2. In a contest that's become known as "The Sandberg Game," Sandberg hit game-tying home runs in the ninth and tenth innings off of what Hall of Fame pitcher?

3. In 1990, Sandberg became only the third second baseman to accomplish what hitting feat?

4. Who did Sandberg replace as manager of the Philadelphia Phillies in August 2013?

5. Sandberg is one of only three players to have seasons of 40 homers and 50 stolen bases in their career. Who are the other two?

Who is the only player to hit a home run out of Wrigley Field and onto the roof of one of the apartment buildings across the street from left field?

Answers

1.

Ivan DeJesus

2.

Bruce Sutter

3.

He became the third second
baseman to hit 40 home
runs in a season.

4.

Charlie Manuel

5.

Brady Anderson and Barry Bonds

Glenallen Hill

FERGIE

1. Beginning in 1967, Ferguson Jenkins won at least 20 games for how many consecutive seasons?

2. Jenkins spent his off-seasons playing for what other athletic team from 1967-69?

3. In 1971, Jenkins became both the first Cub and Canadian to win the National League Cy Young Award. Who is the only other Canadian to win the Cy Young?

4. Jenkins is the only Hall of Famer to have 3,000 strikeouts and fewer than how many walks?

5. Commonly known as Fergie, what other nickname did Jenkins go by?

What Franklin Pierce Adams poem gave fame and notoriety to the Cubs double play combination of Tinker to Evers to Chance?

ANSWERS

1.

Six

2.

The Harlem Globetrotters

3.

Eric Gagne

4.

1,000

5.

Fly

Baseball's Sad Lexicon

SECOND GUESSING

1.
Johnny Bench won the National League MVP Award in 1970. Who finished second in the voting?

2.
Trailing only Ty Cobb, what player who won the 1929 National League MVP as a member of the Cubs, has the second highest career batting average?

3.
What Cubs fan favorite is second in team history with 456 doubles?

4.
Although his time in Chicago was brief, what player who began his career with the Cubs is second all-time in stolen bases to Rickey Henderson?

5.
What pitcher made 343 starts for the Cubs over the course of 10 seasons, which is good for second in team history?

The fans that occupy the general admission outfield seats at Wrigley Field go by what collective moniker?

ANSWERS

1.

Billy Williams

2.

Rogers Hornsby (.358)

3.

Mark Grace

4.

Lou Brock (938)

5.

Rick Reuschel

The Bleacher Bums

MAD DOG

1. What unique situation was Greg Maddux inserted into for his first major league appearance?

2. In 1992, the final season of his first stint with the Cubs, Maddux won the NL Cy Young Award. The honor would be the first of how many consecutive Cy Youngs for him?

3. Popularly known as Mad Dog, Maddux earned what other nickname for his cerebral nature of pitching?

4. After returning to the Cubs in 2004 from the Braves, Maddux recorded his 300th win and 3,000th strikeout against the same team, but in different seasons. What club?

5. In his second farewell from the Cubs, Maddux was traded to the Dodgers during the 2006 trading deadline for whom?

❄ SEASONAL STUMPER ❄

Two weeks before Christmas in 2007, the Cubs signed this Japanese player to a four-year $48 million deal. Holiday season aside, there was no return privilege for this purchase as the outfielder played with unproductive results and eventually, in 2013, made his way to the Tigers - the Hanshin Tigers of Japan. Who is he?

ANSWERS

1.

He was used as a pinch-runner.

2.

Four

3.

The Professor

4.

San Francisco Giants

5.

Cesar Izturis

Seasonal Stumper Answer:

Kosuke Fukudome

THE GREAT HOME RUN CHASE

1. In 1998, Sammy Sosa put himself into contention to break Roger Maris' single season home run record by hitting a record how many homers in the month of June?

2. How many years did it take after Sosa and Mark McGwire toppled Maris' record for it to be broken again?

3. On the night McGwire hit his record-breaking 62nd homer, the Cardinals played the Cubs at Busch Stadium. Off of what Cubs pitcher did McGwire belt his historic shot?

4. True or False? Despite establishing a new single-season home run record in 1998, McGwire still finished second to Sosa in MVP balloting that year.

5. *Sports Illustrated* named McGwire and Sosa co-recipients of what annual award in 1998?

Santa knows rooftops- Do you? The Wrigley Rooftops run along what two streets beyond the outfield fence?

ANSWERS

1.

20

2.

Only three- Barry Bonds hit
73 home runs in 2001.

3.

Steve Trachsel

4.

True

5.

Sportsmen of the Year

Waveland and Sheffield Avenues

His Playing Days Are Numbered

In their history, the Cubs have officially retired just five uniform numbers (one of them is retired for two players.) Match up each Cubs player with his number.

1. Ernie Banks

a. 10

2. Fergie Jenkins/Greg Maddux

b. 14

3. Ryne Sandberg

c. 23

4. Ron Santo

d. 26

5. Billy Williams

e. 31

Wrigley Field was originally scheduled to receive lights in 1941. How come the Cubs did not begin to play night baseball that year?

ANSWERS

1.

b

2.

e

3.

c

4.

a

5.

d

The team donated its lighting
equipment to the War Department in 1941.

BEAR-LY KNEW YA

1. Before becoming an All-Star and World Series winner elsewhere, what player spent just under a season and a half with the Cubs beginning in 1995?

2. After being released by the Padres, what former All-Star and division rival signed with the Cubs in May of 2008 and played 85 games before sitting out the 2009 season?

3. What one-time perennial All-Star outfielder who wore 11 different uniforms over his major league career played 56 games for the Cubs in 2003?

4. In 2007, the Cubs acquired what former All-Star catcher from the Athletics who would appear in 57 games before departing as a free agent the following offseason?

5. Acquired in a July 2001 trade, what veteran nicknamed "The Crime Dog" blasted 42 homer runs during his year and a half Cubs stint?

On Opening Day 1952, what Cub set the tone for his National League MVP-winning season with a grand slam during the team's first game?

ANSWERS

1.

Luis Gonzalez

2.

Jim Edmonds

3.

Kenny Lofton

4.

Jason Kendall

5.

Fred McGriff

Hank Sauer

SILVER SLUGGER

1. The Silver Slugger Award is given out every year to the best hitter at each position in both leagues. The Cubs have had Silver Sluggers at every position except where?

2. In his 2005 Silver Slugger-winning season, Derrek Lee also won what other offensive honor?

3. Who is the only Cubs Silver Slugger recipient to never make an All-Star team?

4. What Cub is the all-time leader at his position for Silver Sluggers?

5. True or False? Despite their Hall of Fame careers, Ernie Banks and Billy Williams never won a Silver Slugger Award.

❄ SEASONAL STUMPER ❄

With just seven shopping days left until Christmas 2010, the Cubs decided to "re-gift" themselves one of the franchise's players of the recent past, Kerry Wood. You may very well know the popular pitcher's nickname, but is it a straightforward "Kid K" or is the letter K spelled backward (as in scorekeeping's called third strike)?

ANSWERS

1.

Shortstop

2.

The National League batting title

3.

Michael Barrett

4.

Ryne Sandberg, 7

5.

True, but that's because the
award wasn't instituted
until 1980, after they retired.

Seasonal Stumper Answer:

Kid K

WHO SAID IT?

1. In reference to Wrigley Field's many day games, what Cubs catcher said, "It's nice to be home for breakfast and it's nice to be home for dinner"?

2. On whether or not Babe Ruth actually called his legendary shot in the 1932 World Series, what Cubs pitcher said, "If he had, I would have knocked him down with the next pitch"?

3. After the Cubs became just the second major league franchise to win 10,000 games, what Cubs infielder said, "It was a tough 10,000 wins. I hope the next 10,000 are easier"?

4. Former Cubs owner Rob Verdi was referencing what company when he said, "I don't know why we bought the Cubs. We already had a perfectly good company softball team"?

5. What former Cub and award-winning broadcaster said of the team's fans, "When you bought your ticket, you could bank on seeing the bottom of the ninth"?

What all-time pinch-hit leader was released by the Cubs after a short stint in 2003, but got the last laugh as part of the Marlins team that beat Chicago in the NLCS later that season?

ANSWERS

1.

Joe Girardi

2.

Charlie Root

3.

Ryan Theriot

4.

The Chicago Tribune Company

5.

Joe Garagiola

Lenny Harris

WEB GEMS

1. Other than 18-time Gold Glove winner Greg Maddux, what other Cubs pitcher, a southpaw, was awarded a Gold Glove in 1964?

2. From 1983 until 1991, what slick fielding Cub won nine consecutive Gold Glove Awards?

3. In 1986, what Cubs catcher who once allowed 21 passed balls in a single season took home the Gold Glove Award?

4. Ernie Banks virtually split his career defensively, playing 11 seasons at first base and nine at shortstop. At which position did he win a Gold Glove?

5. What Gold Glove-winner batted leadoff for the Cubs 1984 NL Eastern Division winners? (Hint: Harry Caray dubbed him and Ryne Sandberg the "Daily Double.")

For 35 seasons, the Cubs have called what city their spring training Cactus League home?

ANSWERS

1.

   Bobby Shantz

2.

   Ryne Sandberg

3.

   Jody Davis

4.

   Shortstop

5.

   Bobby Dernier

Mesa, Arizona

SLAMMIN' SAMMY

1. The Cubs received Sammy Sosa from the cross-town Chicago White Sox in a trade for what All-Star outfielder?

2. Sosa hit 60 or more homers a record three times. How many times did he lead the NL in homers during those "60 or more" seasons?

3. Sosa ran into controversy when he was discovered to be using what illegal item during a 2003 game?

4. With what team did Sosa hit his 609th and final home run?

5. Sosa became eligible for the Hall of Fame in 2013. Did he make it?

Who came first, the Chicago Cubs or the Bears?

ANSWERS

1.

George Bell

2.

None (He won the home run crown in 2000 with 50 and in 2002 with 49.)

3.

A corked bat

4.

The Texas Rangers

5.

No

The Cubs, who began in 1870 while the Bears organization was established in 1919

AWARD TOUR

1. The Cubs have had five rookies honored as the National League Rookie of the Year. Who was the most recent recipient in 2008?

2. In 2013, what Hall of Famer received the Presidential Medal of Freedom, the highest honor awarded to civilians in the United States?

3. In 1962, what Cubs National League Rookie of the Year, a second baseman, became the first rookie to win a Gold Glove?

4. In addition to winning the 1979 National League Cy Young Award, Bruce Sutter also took home what other honor given to relief pitchers that year?

5. What longtime Cub took home both the National League batting title and the National League MVP Award in 1945, Chicago's last pennant winning season?

❄ SEASONAL STUMPER ❄

If you know how many times the name "Santa Claus" appears in *The Night Before Christmas* classic, then you know the uniform number of Cubs Hall of Fame pitcher Grover Cleveland Alexander.

ANSWERS

1.

Geovany Soto

2.

Ernie Banks

3.

Ken Hubbs

4.

National League Rolaids
Relief Man of the Year

5.

Phil Cavarretta

Seasonal Stumper Answer:

None- The name Santa is not mentioned and Alexander
played before the Cubs wore numbers on their jersey.

DOWN ON THE FARM

1. Prior to becoming the Cubs Triple-A minor league affiliate in 1981, the Iowa Cubs went by what name?

2. Before signing in Japan, who set the Iowa Cubs single-season home run record in 2011 with 38 and then made the NL All-Star team in 2012 during a brief stint with the Cubs?

3. The Iowa Cubs are in what league?

4. After his June 2012 call-up, what Cubs rookie became the first player in club history to deliver three game-winning RBIs in his first five games as a Cub?

5. In 2010, what Cubs player became the first major leaguer born in the 1990s after his call-up from Chicago's Double-A affiliate, the Tennessee Smokies?

In 2001, what Cubs pitcher ended the Cincinnati Reds National League record 208-game streak of not being shut out by tossing nine scoreless innings of 1-hit ball: Kerry Wood, Jon Lieber, or Carlos Zambrano?

ANSWERS

1.

Iowa Oaks

2.

Bryan LaHair

3.

Pacific Coast League

4.

Anthony Rizzo

5.

Starlin Castro

Jon Lieber

MIDSUMMER CLASSICS

1. The first All-Star Game was held in Chicago in 1933, in the daytime for obvious reasons. Was it at Wrigley Field or Comiskey Park?

2. Who is the only Cub to be named All-Star Game MVP? (Hint: It was in 1975, the first of four seasons this player would win a batting title, with a .354 average.)

3. Who is the only Cubs pitcher to be named the starter for the National League All-Stars: Charlie Root, Rick Reuschel, or Claude Passeau?

4. Dusty Baker managed the 2003 National League All-Stars in a Cubs uniform even though the Cubs were not the defending NL champions. How come?

5. What Cub won the Home Run Derby in 1990 at Wrigley Field: Andre Dawson, Ryne Sandberg, or Sammy Sosa?

What Cubs All-Star representative recorded the first outfield force-out in an All-Star Game in 53 years in 2010, when he threw out David Ortiz at second base from right field in the ninth inning?

ANSWERS

1. Comiskey Park, where the AL topped the NL, 4-2, in broad daylight because nighttime baseball wasn't introduced until 1935

2. Bill Madlock (He shared game MVP honors in '75 with Jon Matlack of the Mets.)

3. Claude Passeau (1946)

4. Baker managed the pennant-winning San Francisco Giants in 2002 and signed with the Cubs prior to the 2003 season.

5. Ryne Sandberg- Dawson, in 1987, and Sosa, in 2000, are the only other Cubs to have won the Derby.

Marlon Byrd

MULTI-SPORT STUDS

1. What pitcher opted to sign a contract with the Cubs rather than enter the NFL Draft after starring at Notre Dame as a wide receiver?

2. What player who pitched for the 1984 Cubs was a member of the 1973-74 NC State University NCAA Men's Basketball National Championship-winning squad?

3. What Steelers' Super Bowl XL-winning wide receiver and All-Pro punt returner was drafted by the Cubs in 1997?

4. He was the star of TV's *Rifleman* and played 66 games for the Cubs in 1951 after previously playing basketball for the Boston Celtics. Name him.

5. What former Dallas Cowboys and New York Jets quarterback briefly played in the Cubs minor league system before going to play football at the University of Georgia?

Famous for the ivy covering its outfield walls, what happens at Wrigley Field when a batted ball gets stuck in the ivy?

ANSWERS

1.

Jeff Samardzija

2.

Tim Stoddard

3.

Antwaan Randle El

4.

Chuck Connors

5.

Quincy Carter

It is ruled a ground rule double. If the ball
comes out of the ivy it is ruled in play.

LAST LICKS

1. Who was the last Cubs player to wear #42 before Major League Baseball retired the number across the league in honor of Jackie Robinson?

2. What Cubs manager is the author of a book titled *Nice Guys Finish Last*?

3. Who was the last Cub to hit for the cycle?

4. He began his career with the Cubs in 1986. Some 26 years later with Colorado, he achieved his final victory at 49, the oldest MLB pitcher ever to win a game. Name him.

5. After announcing his retirement prior to the game, what Cubs pitcher struck out the final and only batter he faced in his last appearance in May of 2012?

❄ SEASONAL STUMPER ❄

On December 23, 1997, the Cubs received an early unexpected Christmas gift when they acquired what player, who would surprisingly receive MVP votes at the end of the season, from the Philadelphia Phillies for Doug Glanville?

ANSWERS

1.

Glenallen Hill

2.

Leo Durocher

3.

Mark Grace (May 9, 1993)

4.

Jamie Moyer

5.

Kerry Wood

Seasonal Stumper Answer:

Mickey Morandini

TEAM TRIVIA

Okay, so you think you know the Cubs pretty well, but how about their opponents? See if you can identify each of the major league teams from the following questions.

1. What team has won the most games in a regular season since the turn of the century?

2. Minnie Minoso made a brief appearance for this team in 1980, making it the fifth decade that he played Major League Baseball, the only player since 1900 to do so. Name the club.

3. This Hall of Famer's #29 has been retired by the Angels and one other club. Can you name the player and the team?

4. In 1959, Harvey Haddix threw the longest perfect game in major league history, 12 innings. Unfortunately he lost the no-hitter and the game, 1-0, in the 13th to the Milwaukee Braves. Haddix was pitching for what team?

5. What team played at Wrigley Field in its first year of existence?

True or False? There was only one man to ever hit a ball that struck the Wrigley Field scoreboard and that man was nicknamed Slammin' Sammy.

6. What club became the first wild card team in major league history to win a World Series, in 1997?

7. What team changed its name for a while during the cold war with Russia?

8. Who did the St. Louis Browns become?

9. In 1965, Bert Campaneris became the first major leaguer to play an inning at each of the nine defensive positions in one game. With what team did he achieve this feat?

10. This club is one of only two teams to originate in California. They have never won a World Series and are the only MLB team that's never had a pitcher throw a no-hitter. Name them.

11. Wade Boggs was the first player to hit a home run for his 3,000th hit. What team was he playing for at the time?

12. In 1965, they became the first MLB team to play their home games in an indoor park.

True- Slammin' Sammy Snead, the legendary golfer, used a 4-iron from home plate to launch the shot before the Cubs season opener on April 17, 1951.

13. Andres Galarraga hit one of the longest homers in big league history for this team— a 529-foot tape measure job against the Marlins at Pro Player Stadium in 1997.

14. Name the last major league franchise to relocate from one city to another.

15. On September 10, 1963, three Alou brothers— Jesus, Matty, and Felipe —all batted in a row for what team?

16. The New York Yankees have won the most World Series. What team is a distant second?

17. The first African-American manager in MLB history was hired by what team?

18. What team was managed by its owner for a single game?

19. Who was selected the 2004 "Sportsman of the Year" by *Sports Illustrated*?

20. What franchise won a World Series title in only its fourth year of existence, 2001?

Who is the only man to play in a World Series at both Comiskey Park and Wrigley Field?

21. What team has lost the most games in a single season?

22. When this team's state of the art baseball only ballpark opened in 1962, it had no water fountains! Name the team.

23. Not only was Harmon Killebrew the first Minnesota Twin to make it to the Hall of Fame- he was also the first player on what other club to make it to the Hall?

24. What team, since the inception of the American League in 1901, became the first club to switch leagues?

25. Name the team that holds the record for most home runs in a game in major league history.

26. Its present owner is the founder of Little Caesar's pizza. Its former owner is the founder of Domino's pizza. What team is this?

27. Hall of Famer Ted Williams was the very first manager for what team in 1972?

Babe Ruth

28. Name the only team in Major League Baseball history to win five consecutive World Series.

29. This team has the distinction of being the franchise with the longest continuous use of the same nickname in the same city in the history of American professional sports.

The entire 1969 Cubs infield made the
National League All-Star squad. Name the four players.

ANSWERS

1. The Seattle Mariners, 116, in 2001 (tying the MLB record with the Chicago Cubs, who also won 116 way back in 1906)

2. Chicago White Sox

3. Rod Carew, by the Twins

4. Pittsburgh Pirates

5. The Los Angeles Angels, in 1961- Wrigley Field in Los Angeles, that is. (The Cubs played at the West Side Grounds in Chicago before moving into *the* Wrigley Field.)

6. Miami (then Florida) Marlins

7. The Cincinnati Reds (as in Soviets) changed their name to the Red Legs.

8. The Baltimore Orioles

9. The Oakland Athletics

10. San Diego Padres

11. The Tampa Bay Rays (then Devil Rays)

Ernie Banks (1B), Glenn Beckert (2B), Don Kessinger (SS) and Ron Santo (3B)